"Mathematical ability aside, every reader of this book will benefit from us m..... .nd concise tactics for tackling math anxiety. I wish I had a copy for each and every one of my students."

Michelle Scharpen, High School Math Teacher, Prague High School, Prague, MN

"This is a wonderful book to convince students that they can do math. After exploring this book and all of its resources, students will want to embrace math rather than avoid it. Using the exploding field of drone technology to entice them and keep them interested is genius. Students will see the importance of math and the sequential unfolding of the examples in each chapter. If teachers use this book with all of the research and discussion ideas available to them, it will be a game changer. Most importantly, a way for students to engage in their own learning and advance the conversation in the classroom and outside the classroom in areas they may not even think of exploring on their own."

Joy Dimaggio, retired Coordinator Of School Counseling k-12 Enfield Public Schools, Enfield, CT

"I liked the activities at the end of the chapters."

Tucker Jones, grade 8 student, 1st Sgt. Kevin A. Dupont Middle School, Chicopee, MA

"I liked the statistics and the facts about drone racing. And I liked the idea of owning a drone racing warehouse to see everyone's different drones and their skills. I will tell my friends about this book."

Audrey Amaral, grade 7 student, Saint Mary's Parish School, Westfield, MA

CRUSH MATH
ANXIETY
WITH DRONES

CRUSH MATH ANXIETY WITH DRONES

Succeed In Math By Nurturing A Growth Mindset Through Drone Stories

Jeanne Holmberg

Cover Designed by Muhammad Affan

Cover Design by Muhammad Affan – The TechFlames
Images by Microsoft Word and unsplash.com
ISBN-13: 979-8-9850111-0-4

WARNING

To Get The Most Out Of This Book, You Need
To Talk About It.

DEDICATION

This book is dedicated to all students who are struggling to see the beauty of mathematics and to all teachers who are struggling to help them see.

AUTHOR'S NOTE

The growth mindset, conceived by Carol Dweck (2006) and colleagues, offers exciting educational opportunities that are redefining classrooms and learning. Simply stated, the growth mindset is the belief that a person can develop their basic abilities over time through dedication, hard work, and practice. In contrast, a fixed mindset is the belief that a person cannot further develop their basic abilities. Unfortunately, many students fall into the fixed mindset regarding their math abilities. There can be many reasons for this, ranging from unfortunate personal experiences to societal implications. The good news is that the research findings have emerged from scientific journals and are being put into practice. Students who have math teachers and learning opportunities that have implemented growth mindset strategies have already reaped the benefits (Boaler, 2019).

The transition to high school is an optimal time to develop, practice, or enrich a growth mindset. To further the growth mindset movement, young teens need to hear about the current research. They need encouragement. They need to be motivated by real life applications that interest them. They need to see the links between the big ideas and the applications. They need to absorb concepts with a multidimensional approach. They need to see the cumulative nature of mathematics. They need to avoid the frustration of computation errors and common misunderstandings that are so easy to fix. They need to question, discuss, and collaborate. They need to explore big ideas without time constraints. By including all of these features, this book encourages young teens to take an active role in nurturing a growth mindset and developing their math abilities, even if math has been a difficult subject for them.

Statistics (US) indicate a grade 8 math proficiency of 34% (CER, 2019). To promote equal opportunity and math mastery, especially for low income and poor performing districts, there is a dire need to promote the growth mindset and to cite the recent neurological evidence that all students can learn math. This book uses growth mindset strategies to inspire young teens to develop their math skills, build their confidence, and prepare for the trending job market.

To captivate interest, the reader is immersed in the exploding field of drone technology. Applications that interest teens are explored in three ways – stories, big ideas and additional insights. Each one may appeal to different students. Together, they encourage readers to make connections and strengthen understanding. Numerous related links provide video entertainment and positive messaging.

"Everyone can learn math to high levels."

Jo Boaler

TABLE OF CONTENTS

ACKNOWLEDGMENTS

To my husband who has always supported my efforts – I love you.
To my mom who always gave me sharpened new pencils for test days.
To my stellar colleagues at Enfield High School who are all about the kids.

CHAPTER 1

EVERYONE CAN LEARN MATH

Our brains have an amazing ability to develop new skills and learn new things. This amazing potential that we all have and how to achieve it is well documented in a book called "Limitless Mind: Learn, Lead, and Live Without Barriers" by Jo Boaler. Her research documents both cutting-edge science and practical experience in the classroom. Her work has such a positive message for all of us. Each one of us have limitless potential. Your mind has limitless potential. You have limitless potential.

Exploring "Crush Math Anxiety With Drones, Succeed In Math By Nurturing A Growth Mindset Through Drone Stories" is a promising first step to realizing your potential. Do not be discouraged if math has been a difficult subject for you. Recent brain science proves that "everyone can learn mathematics to high levels".[1] But believing in yourself is key. You need to believe that your basic abilities can be developed through dedication, hard work, and practice. A famous psychologist, Carol Dweck, coined a term for this. It is called having a *growth mindset*.

Researchers have developed strategies to help you develop a growth mindset. Growth mindset strategies to increase math potential are well documented in another inspiring book by Jo Boaler, "Mathematical Mindsets: Unleashing Students' Potential through Creative Math, Inspiring Messages and Innovative Teaching". These strategies have been successful in helping students succeed in math. Your best math teachers will stay on top of educational research like this. They will try different approaches to help you succeed. But you need to do your part too. Believe that you can do math and work at it. This book will help you. It will help you practice growth mindset strategies. It will help you succeed in math.

Succeeding in math is important now. Math skills will help you to understand our world and to build a career. And mathematics will grow even more important in your future. Advances in technology demand a workforce with increased math skills. Be determined to get the most out of your high school math experience. Put in the effort and allow yourself to struggle. "Scientists now know that the best times for brain growth and change are when people are working on challenging content, making mistakes, correcting them, moving on, making more mistakes, always working in areas of high challenge."[2] Think of challenging content as a healthy workout for your brain. Think of mistakes as an opportunity to learn something new. Think of correcting mistakes as a memory file so that you will be less likely to make those same mistakes again. By applying a growth mindset such as this, you can be successful in mathematics. With the growth mindset, 'I am not a math person' is an unacceptable excuse.

"Begin to see mathematical reasoning in terms of logical reasoning. After all, that's exactly what it is: mathematical reasoning is merely logical reasoning that is quantifiable, that is, reasoning to which numbers can be attached."[3] The following excerpt from "Mathematical Mindsets, Unleashing Students' Potential Through Creative Math" by Jo Boaler also describes the logical basis of mathematics but with an updated twist.

> When people are asked about how mathematics is used in the world, they usually think of numbers and calculations – of working out mortgages or sale prices – but mathematical thinking is so much more. Mathematics is at the center of thinking about how to spend the day, how many events and jobs can fit into the day, what size of space can be used to fit equipment or turn a car around, how likely events are to happen, knowing how tweets are amplified and how many people they reach. The world respects people who can calculate

quickly, but the fact is, some people can be very fast with numbers and not be able to do great things with them, and others, who are very slow and make many mistakes, go on to do something amazing with mathematics. The powerful thinkers in today's world are not those who can calculate fast, as used to be true; fast calculations are now fully automated, routine, and uninspiring. The powerful thinkers are those who make connections, think logically, and use space, data, and numbers creatively.[4]

In short, this excerpt tells us that the future workplace will demand innovators who can think logically, link data and ideas and use them creatively.

If you are interested in Science, Technology, Engineering and Mathematics (STEM) fields, developing your mathematics skills is especially important. "A knowledge of mathematics is, in fact, an intellectual gatekeeper, or better yet, gateway, into STEM fields. For those who are going to make contributions in these fields, mathematics is vital. And it is growing in importance as the sciences, and even the social sciences, develop."[5] Simply put, math is important now, and it is growing in importance for more and more fields of study. Strong math skills are needed to get accepted into a college STEM program. Strong math skills are also needed to be prepared for the required courses in the STEM program after you are accepted.

Did you know that mathematics can strongly affect how much money you can earn? "High-paying STEM jobs can be the way out of poverty for students. In the past, students who lived in poverty may have taken jobs in manufacturing or other trades. Many of those jobs are disappearing, leaving workers back in poverty. STEM jobs, on the other hand, are everywhere, and the tech industry shows no signs of slowing down. Even as certain STEM trends come and go, we can expect to see the overall number of jobs in STEM fields increase."[6]

What if you are not interested in the STEM fields? "Math will be more represented in the future. Whether we like that or not, math is becoming an increasingly important factor in a variety of industries. Future journalists and politicians will speak less and analyze more. Future police and military personnel will use technology that is certainly an invention of scientists. Teachers and nurses will also rely on numbers and technology. Future mechanics and carpenters will use optimization electronics and analysis as much as they will use a hammer and a wrench."[7] Because society embraces technology, similar messages are common. In short, "Having STEM skills can also help students in non-STEM careers. Technology has become a part of almost every job."[8]

Whatever career(s) you decide to pursue, have you ever thought about what skills you will need to thrive in a global economy? The list below is condensed from "The 10 Vital Skills You Will Need for the Future of Work"[9] by Bernard Marr, *Forbes* contributor. *Forbes* is a company that defines themselves as 'a global media company, focusing on business, investing, technology, entrepreneurship, leadership, and lifestyle.' As of spring 2020, *Forbes* magazine has an audience of 5.8 million readers. The ten vital skills are listed below.

1. Creativity
2. Emotional intelligence (EQ)
3. Analytical (critical) thinking
4. Active learning with a growth mindset
5. Judgement and decision making
6. Interpersonal communication skills
7. Leadership
8. Diversity and cultural intelligence
9. Technology skills
10. Embracing change

Did any of these skills surprise you? As our world changes, so must our skill sets. Don't get caught with outdated skills. At this time, robots cannot compete with humans on creativity. When robots can compete with humans on creativity, the most vital people skills will likely need to change again.

Don't forget to check out the resources at the end of this chapter. Some of the Ted Talks videos are about math and some of them are about high school or life in general. Choose what interests you the most. They are truly inspirational. You can become anything you want to be. Aim high.

Discussion Prompts:

- High School is a great time to re-invent yourself academically – if you want to. Do you agree or disagree? Why or why not?
- How do you react when you have difficulty on an assignment or an assessment? What can you do to improve your reaction or your outcome?
- What subject areas interest you the most? What careers might tie into those areas?
- Go back and look again at the scroll design above the chapter title. Discuss a possible analogy between this design and mathematics.

Curious? Research Prompts:

- Growth Mindset
- STEM or STEAM
- Career(s) that might interest you
- Optimization (in general) and/or optimization electronics

Learning Task: *"What Does the Growth Mindset Mean To You?"*

Nurture Your Growth Mindset By Engaging In This Short Activity

"What Does the Growth Mindset Mean To You?"

Note that discussion is so important when exploring these activities. Discuss or compare your responses with peers or family members.

(Complete one or both. Your choice.)

Sketch a logo advertising the growth mindset and what it means to you.

Write a paragraph about the growth mindset and what it means to you.

Note: The activities at the end of each chapter can be used for peer discussion, class explorations, summer reading list participants, teen clubs, home schooling, or other. If needed, most of the answers can then be easily verified on-line. With technology, knowledge is at your fingertips. Practice your research skills. Personal choice or opinion answers will vary.

Ted Talks

Ted Talks are free videos by expert speakers. These videos share ideas on a wide selection of topics that are inspirational and informational. "While the brilliance of TED Talks are nothing new, it can be hard, even in intellectual circles, to find people willing to talk about math for an extended period of time. This is despite the fact that numbers rule the world and are the language of the universe and quite possibly time immortal." (D. Chance)

A sampling of Ted Talks is provided below. Some of them are about math. Some of them are about high school, education or life in general. Find what interests you. Enjoy their wisdom.

For middle school age students who hate math:
https://likeabubblingbrook.com/ted-talks-for-middle-school/

For people who hated math in high school:
https://www.ted.com/playlists/251/talks_for_people_who_hated_mat

To get teens excited about math:
http://www.mathsinsider.com/ted-ed/

Ten talks about numbers: (D. Chance)
https://www.accountingschoolguide.com/10-awesome-ted-talks-about-numbers/

Talks by brilliant kids and teens:
https://www.ted.com/playlists/129/ted_under_20

Inspirational talks for high school in general:
https://content.wisestep.com/ted-talks-for-high-school-students/

Talks that every educator should check out:
https://www.opencolleges.edu.au/informed/features/50-ted-talks-every-educator-should-check-out/

CHAPTER 2

DID A DRONE DELIVER YOUR TAKE-OUT ORDER?

One example of an exciting STEM field that is exploding is drone technology. These aircraft without pilots on board are populating our air space all over the world. Drones are used in commercial, agricultural, military, and private enterprise. Check out these interesting drone statistics:[1]

- Business and government spent 13 billion dollars on drones in 2020.
- There are over 1,782,000 recreational drones registered in the United States.
- Sales of consumer drones in the United States exceeded 1.25 billion dollars in 2020.
- By 2024, the drone market is predicted to be worth around $43 billion.
- The number of jobs operating drones in the industry will reach 422,000 by 2021.

After citing these statistics and more, the author concludes, "Drones are everywhere these days. Next time you are at a concert or at any type of open-venue event, just look up and you will see what I mean."[2]

Some colleges now offer programs in this specialized field. The University of North Dakota (UND) is one example. In this program at UND (2021), "you'll gain the expertise in unmanned aircraft to execute and manage applications in the military, firefighting, disaster relief, law enforcement, surveillance, aerial photography, transports and future uses of this rapidly evolving area."[3]

Research and development in drone technology are also being promoted by world-wide competitions which award large prizes, one of which is one million dollars.[4] To get students who are interested in drone technology started, there are even smaller competitions for high school age and younger students.[5]

A typical drone has four rotors. The rotors operate much like a fan. Because they have four rotors, they are often called drone quadcopters. The mathematics that power the drones, however, are in the microcontrollers. Drones can move forward, backward, hover, turn, climb and descend by varying the power to these four rotors. This allows a skilled pilot to fly in just about any direction.

On a trial basis, UPS has partnered with CVS to deliver customer medications.[6] FedEx has partnered with Walgreens to deliver Kids Snack Packs and other merchandise to select locations.[7] UPS, Google, and Amazon delivery services have already won flight approval by the FAA to operate drone airlines.[8] Public safety is a concern, but parachutes may be the solution. In 2014, Amazon applied for a patent from the U.S. Patent and Trademark Office for "a method to guide packages released from drones safely to the ground."[9] In 2017, Amazon was granted this patent. Amazon said that "landing a drone takes more time and energy than releasing a package from high in the sky. If Amazon's drones don't land in yards, this prevents potentially dangerous collisions between the drones and any people, pets, or objects in a customer's yard."[10] With all of this in mind, how long do you think it will be before a drone delivers your take-out order?

Three very interesting applications of drone technology include drone racing, aerial displays and cinematography. "Drone racing is the fastest, craziest, most intense sport you have never heard of."[11] Imagine how exciting it would be to watch 16 pilots on the ground flying drones in the air at speeds of 90 miles per hour in a 64,000-capacity stadium. The world record as of this writing is 163.5 miles per hour.[12] Imagine the adrenaline of the pilots and their crews. Quick decisions, dexterity, good judgement, and well maintained equipment is a must. "There has now even been a game released on Xbox and Steam called 'The DRL SIM', a true-to-life drone racing game with real-life drone physics where gamers and pilots can hone their skills, racing through real-life circuits. This sport is hitting the big time, and it is only five years old."[13]

A different skill set is needed for the synchronization of drones in aerial displays that are far more sophisticated than fireworks. People, animals, buildings, objects – artwork in the sky. Imagine an event with 3,051 drones. This dazzling event broke the Guinness World Records title. "For the finale, the drones formed a giant Mars rover in order to express the desire of all mankind for the exploration of the universe, the formation revealed a giant Mars rover."[14]

Drone cinematography, another form of art, adds thrilling footage to popular films. As you stream your favorite films, do you think the footage would be as up close and personal if the videographers had to film with a personal action camera, a cable camera or from a helicopter?

It is an exciting world out there and you are a part of it. The high school years are an ideal time to improve your skills and explore new ideas. If you are curious and want to learn more about drones, several resources are provided to get you started. To quickly find what you want, they are listed by categories in alphabetical order at the end of this chapter. The videos of drone racing, aerial drone displays, and movie scenes are especially fun to watch. If an introduction preceded these clips, it would need to say that all of this is brought to you by mathematics. Mathematics is the universal language that propels technology forward.

Discussion Prompts:

- Predict how long will it be before you have the opportunity to receive packages that are delivered by drones. What influenced your prediction?
- Which application of drone technology interests you the most – drone racing, aerial displays, or cinematography? Why?
- If you decided you wanted to build a drone, what would you do first? What steps would you take after that? If you struggled along the way, what would you do?

Curious? Research Prompts:

- Drone competitions
- Explore some of the greatest action scenes in recent films. What makes them so intense and exciting? How were they filmed? If you were the cinematographer, would you do anything different?
- Why is mathematics considered a 'universal language'?
- What is the FAA? What is a drone airline? Why is safety a concern?

Learning Task: *"Getting Comfortable With Large Numbers"*

Nurture Your Growth Mindset By Engaging
In This Short Activity

"Getting Comfortable With Large Numbers"

Note that discussion is so important when exploring these activities. Discuss or compare your responses with peers or family members.

1. How many zeroes are there in "one billion"?

2. How do you write "one billion" in scientific notation?

3. Which is the largest number – "one billion" or "one million" or "one trillion"?

4. Can you rank these numbers (one billion, one million, and one trillion) from smallest to largest using inequality symbols?

5. How do you write 1.25 billion dollars using only digits (without the word "billion")?

6. How do you write 1.25 billion in scientific notation?

7. In your opinion, is it helpful to use commas when expressing very large numbers like 1.25 billion using only digits (not using words)? Why or why not?

8. If you used a tennis ball to represent the magnitude of the number 1.25 billion, what items would you use to represent the magnitude of the other numbers listed in the drone statistics provided at the start of this chapter: 13 billion; 1,782,000; 43 billion; and 422,000?

9. Sketch a number line showing the relative placement of all the numbers listed in the drone statistics from above. Your choice: 1) write the numbers as shown above on your number line 2) write the numbers

using only digits and commas 3) write the numbers in scientific notation 4) write the numbers in all of these ways.

Note: The activities at the end of each chapter can be used for peer discussion, class explorations, summer reading list participants, teen clubs, home schooling, or other. If needed, most of the answers can then be easily verified on-line. With technology, knowledge is at your fingertips. Practice your research skills. Personal choice or opinion answers will vary.

Drones and Related Resources

AERIAL DRONE DISPLAYS:

Mars rover aerial display:
https://www.techeblog.com/largest-drone-display-china-guinness-world-records/

Behind the making of a synchronized drone light show:
https://www.cbsnews.com/news/synchronized-drones-intel-light-show/

Holiday light show sponsored by Walmart:
https://www.ksat.com/features/2020/12/04/this-holiday-drone-light-show-might-be-the-coolest-thing-youll-see-this-holiday-season/

https://corporate.walmart.com/newsroom/2020/11/23/walmart-lights-up-the-sky-with-all-new-holiday-drone-light-show

Cooler than fireworks:
https://www.forbes.com/sites/grrlscientist/2020/06/30/drone-light-shows-way-cooler-than-fireworks/

DRONE COMPETITIONS:

Drone racing has become one of the fastest growing sports in the world:
https://www.thesportsman.com/features/28million-fans-100-000-prizes-welcome-to-the-crazy-world-of-elite-drone-racing (S. Lillicrap, Dec 2020)

Competition for teens:
https://drobotscompany.com/drone-stem-competition-grades-1-12-high-school-kids-teens/

One million dollar prize:
https://dronexchallenge2020.com/

National competition at University of North Dakota April 2022:

UAS Pilots from across the nation will travel to Grand Forks, ND to test their skills and determine the fastest pilot in the nation. This is the second year UND will host the CDRC. The event is tentatively scheduled for April 2022.

UND is the world-renowned leader in aviation, and the first university to offer a degree in unmanned aircraft systems.

The championships will be held in the UND High Performance Center. Normally an indoor training facility for the Fighting Hawks athletics teams, the facility will be transformed again into a championship drone racing course. The HPC is a 200,000-square-foot, climate controlled facility that features bleacher seating and space for pilots and sponsors.

https://und.edu/research/rias/cdrc/

DRONE RACING:

https://www.youtube.com/watch?v=pZ0viMxYDA4

https://dronedj.com/2021/01/05/leonardos-second-ai-drone-competition-communication-is-key/

HISTORY OF DRONES:

A Beginners Guide to Drones, UAVs and ROVs
http://ptgmedia.pearsoncmg.com/images/9780789755988/samplepages/9780789755988.pdf

The history of drones in ten milestones by Luke Dormehl, September 11, 2018
https://www.digitaltrends.com/cool-tech/history-of-drones/

STEM Exploratory Lesson 1History of Drone Aviation (research and construct a presentation) http://emslopez.weebly.com/uploads/5/2/3/6/52362037/lesson_1_history_of_drones.pdf

DRONES YESTERDAY, TODAY, AND TOMORROW – History of Flight
https://www.flightjournal.com/wp-content/uploads/2018/01/Drones_throughout_history.pdf

Ultimate List of Drone Stats for 2021:
https://www.phillybyair.com/blog/drone-stats/

MOVIE CLIPS, VIDEOS AND DRONE CINEMATOGRAPHY:

https://www.studiobinder.com/blog/best-drone-video-footage/

https://www.dronethusiast.com/drone-videos-that-blow-your-mind/

https://www.youtube.com/watch?v=bLZRG4d3iUk

https://www.productionhub.com/blog/post/drones-and-their-impact-in-the-film-industry

PUBLIC SAFETY AND DRONES:

https://www.faa.gov/uas/public_safety_gov/public_safety_toolkit/media/Public_Safety_Drone_Playbook.pdf

TOP DRONE SERVICE PROVIDERS IN 2020:

https://droneii.com/drone-service-provider-ranking-2020

TRIALS WITH COMMERCIAL DRONES:

Drones can already deliver coffee in Australia -Wing (subsidiary of Alphabet Inc.)
https://www.youtube.com/watch?v=prhDrfUgpB0

Wing (company)
https://en.wikipedia.org/wiki/Wing_(company)

Drone deliveries in Virginia:
https://www.businesswire.com/news/home/20190919005574/en/

https://news.walgreens.com/press-releases/general-news/walgreens-will-be-first-retailer-in-us-to-test-on-demand-drone-delivery-service-with-wing.htm

Walgreens partners with Wing to deliver food staples and other household products:
https://www.walgreensbootsalliance.com/news-media/our-stories/during-covid-19-drone-delivery-is-really-taking-off

CVS partners with UPS to deliver prescriptions:
https://www.cnn.com/videos/business/2019/11/06/ups-cvs-drone-delivery-prescription-orig.cnn-business

https://www.cnbc.com/2019/10/21/ups-partners-with-cvs-to-develop-drone-delivery-service-for-prescriptions.html

https://www.thedenverchannel.com/news/national/coronavirus/ups-cvs-will-use-drones-to-deliver-medication-to-nations-largest-retirement-community

VIDEO GAMES DRONES:

https://news.xbox.com/en-us/2020/09/28/exhilarating-drone-racing-worlds/

WHAT ARE THE BEST DRONES?

https://dronesfy.com/top-best-drones-under-300-guide/

https://www.pcmag.com/picks/the-best-drones

Drones with cameras:
https://droneswatch.org/drones-with-camera/

19

CHAPTER 3

DRONE STORIES AND
HIGH SCHOOL MATH

"Crush Math Anxiety With Drones, Succeed In Math By Nurturing A Growth Mindset Through Drone Stories" previews some of the big ideas you will explore in your high school math courses. These big ideas come to life in playful short stories about drones.

To get started, fast forward ten years. Imagine yourself as the owner of a drone racing warehouse. Teens buy monthly memberships to practice their drone racing skills in your warehouse. In Chapters 4-8, a short story about your drone racing business comes to life. Each story will show you how you can use mathematics to help your business succeed. The big ideas related to each story are explained. Any needed computations are modeled for you. In Chapters 4-6, additional insights about common misunderstandings are also explained. Each format, the short stories, the big ideas, and the additional insights may appeal to different students. Together, the three formats encourage students to make connections and strengthen understanding. Any insights you gain will build confidence in your math abilities, even if math has been a difficult subject for you.

While you are exploring high school mathematics, you might also be busy with other things that are very important to you, such as social connections, sports, and/or entertainment. Keeping this in mind, content in this book is brief by design. To get even more out of the time you are investing in reading this book, consider organizing a small group of friends to read this book also. Or, ask your math teacher if it can become an exploratory station in your class or a summer reading option. After each chapter, discuss what you have read. You might be able to explain something to a friend that they did not quite understand, or they might be able to explain something to you. Discussing math in your own words without even needing to write anything down can ease math anxiety and clarify understanding. After finishing this book and seeing a big picture preview of high school mathematics, "Crush Math Anxiety With Drones, Succeed In Math By Nurturing A Growth Mindset Through Drone Stories" can also be used as a reference whenever you need to feel more confident in your math skills. Knowing what math can do for you can help you in both life and career, even if you are not the person or the program actually doing the math computations.

As you read each chapter, always remember that you have much more potential than you probably give yourself credit for. Read and absorb the excerpt below written by Marilyn vos Savant, credited by the *Guinness Book of World Records* with the highest IQ ever recorded.

As intricate a mass as your brain is, you are still using only a fraction of its potential power. The human brain can be compared to that tough little ant with the high hopes, carrying a rubber tree plant many times its own weight. Even neuroscientists, who study the brain professionally, cannot place exact limits on the brain's capabilities…

However, one thing is certain. You can be smarter tomorrow than you are today. The mind can stretch-it can be strengthened, toned, and conditioned to perform miracles for you…[1]

Whenever you need additional inspiration, go back and reread that excerpt. If a tough little ant with high hopes can exceed expectations, so can you.

As you read this book, remember to relax, read slowly, and keep an open mind. Go back and reread any part you need to. You are not being timed. Your best high school math teachers will allow you time to struggle so that you can figure some things out on your own. Struggling to make your own discoveries in your own way leads to a deeper and longer lasting understanding. The examples in this book simply give you a platform to leap from.

Discussion Prompts:

- What does this sentence mean to you? "Knowing what math can do for you can help you in both life and career, even if you are not the person or the program actually doing the math computations." Do you agree or disagree? Why or why not?
- Can you invent a word or phrase that lessens your frustration when you struggle in math? Something that will motivate you to keep trying.
- In your opinion, what does it mean to "keep an open mind"? Do you think keeping an open mind would help you to succeed in learning new math skills? Why or why not?

Curious? Research Prompts:

- Professional drone racing
- How do you build a drone?
- How do you start a business?

Learning Task: *"Keeping Up With Technology and Making Predictions"*

Nurture Your Growth Mindset By Engaging
In This Short Activity

"Keeping Up With Technology and Making Predictions"

Note that discussion is so important when exploring these activities. Discuss and compare your responses with peers or family members.

(Your choice. Write, draw, or make a collage.)

1. What year will it be in ten years?

2. How old will you be in ten years?

3. Research a list of at least five new technologies that have occurred in the past ten years.

4. Predict what new technologies will emerge in the next ten years.

5. Describe what you think your life will be like in ten years.

Note: The activities at the end of each chapter can be used for peer discussion, class explorations, summer reading list participants, teen clubs, home schooling, or other. If needed, most of the answers can then be easily verified on-line. With technology, knowledge is at your fingertips. Practice your research skills. Personal choice or opinion answers will vary.

CHAPTER 4

WHAT IS MODELING?

What if...you could fast forward ten years? You now own and operate a warehouse for teen drone operators to practice their indoor flight skills. It can take years before your new businesses starts to earn a profit. How long can you keep paying the bills before you start making money?

To get your business started, you needed to pay a large sum of money to purchase the warehouse. Thankfully, your investors helped you with this. You also have monthly costs to run your business. A few examples of the costs you pay each month might be heat/air conditioning, lighting, payroll for your employees, insurance, and advertising. The initial cost of the warehouse and your monthly costs will certainly add up. And how much money will you make? Your total income is the total amount of money you collect from the drone operators who purchase monthly memberships for the use of your warehouse.

You will be pleased when you are finally taking in more money than you are paying out. When your total income is larger than your total costs, you are finally making money. Math skills can help you to predict how long it will be before you are finally making money. A graph of the total cost equation and the total income equation will show this. Every graph tells a story. In this example, the graph would show when you are losing money, when you are making money, and even when your total costs are equal to your total income. Financially, can you survive on your savings until your business is finally making money? A graph of the cost and income equations can help you figure this out.

Let's add in some details. Suppose you determined that each month you take in $5,000 from membership fees. What would your total income be after two months? After ten months? Can you write an equation that would represent total income for any number of months?

You also determined that you spend $3,000 each month to run your business. In addition, you paid a one-time fee of $98,000 to purchase the warehouse. What would your total costs be for two months? For ten months? Can you write an equation that would represent total costs for any number of months?

If you struggle with these exercises, don't struggle alone. Help each other out. Brainstorm and discuss. How do you represent "any number of months"? If this is easy for you, how can you explain your thought process to someone else? A bit later, you can check your equations. No worries if you don't get it right. Making mistakes shows that you are trying.

 What are the big ideas wrapped up in this story?

- **Using Variables to Represent Numbers**

Were you able to come up with the equations below? If not, can you explain them now? Note that in both the cost equation and the income equation, the variable "x" is used to represent any number of months. You are in command of these equations. If you were concerned about the next three years, you can plug in any numbers from zero to 36 months to determine your projected income and costs for the number of months you have chosen.

Your total income is represented by the following equation:
$$I = \$5,000x$$

Your total costs to operate your business are modeled by the following equation:
$$C = \$3,000x + \$98,000$$

- **Equations**

The income equation shows the total amount of money you have collected from the monthly memberships. If you wanted to know your total income after 6 months, you plug in 6 for the "x" and multiply by $5,000.

$$I = \$5,000x$$
$$\text{If } x = 6 \text{ months, then } I = \$5,000(6)$$
$$I = \$30,000$$

Interpret your solution: over a 6 month period, you will collect $30,000 in income.

The cost equation shows your total costs for operating your business. For example, if you wanted to know your total costs for 6 months, you would multiply the costs you pay each month ($3,000) by 6. Note that the cost equation also shows an additional cost of $98,000 which is not multiplied by "x". This large dollar amount is not multiplied by the variable "x" because you only pay this amount once. It is not a monthly cost. It is the amount you paid to purchase the warehouse. Notice how much larger your total costs are after 6 months compared to your total income after 6 months. It can be very difficult to get a new business going.

$$C = \$3,000x + \$98,000$$
$$\text{If } x = 6 \text{ months, then } C = \$3,000(6) + \$98,000$$
$$C = \$18,000 + \$98,000$$
$$C = \$116,000$$

Interpret your solution: Your total costs for owning and operating your business for 6 months is $116,000.

- **Functions and Modeling**

The income and cost equations above are also called functions. These functions model the story of your income and your costs. Functions and modeling can be used to make predictions or to make decisions. For example, can you afford to stay in business much longer? Or, when will my total costs be equal to my total income? And why is this called the "break-even" point?

Mathematics is a flexible tool to help you solve problems and make decisions. When you begin to understand one example of modeling, such as the cost and income equations, you can then apply what you know to so many other applications. Linking new challenges to concepts that you already know will help you to make many new discoveries in mathematics.

 Error analysis.

My own students have taught me many things. What additional insights can you gain from these examples? Some students have said:

- *3,000x doesn't look like multiplication because there is no multiplication symbol there. It looks like I have 3,000 letter x's.* This student has a good point. It is easy to fix though. In mathematics, "no symbol", like in this example, is just another way of showing multiplication.

- C = 3,000x + 98,000 *is an equation but how can I solve this equation if I do not even know what number "x" is?* This student actually wants to evaluate "C" after they plug in a value for "x". This is not the same thing as solving for "C". This equation is already solved for "C". We know what "C" is.

"C" is 3,000x + 98,000. In other words, 3,000x + 98,000 is just another name, like a nickname, for "C".

- *If I am losing money when I pay my bills, why are my total costs going up instead of down?* This student is asking a great question. If you buy a new shirt for $25.00, you do not say that it cost you -$25.00. By using the word cost, you are indicating that you are paying out that amount of money. The money is not coming in. In the cost equation, you are paying out $3,000 each month for your operating expenses and you paid a one-time amount of $98,000 for the warehouse. We do not use negative signs for these dollar amounts. As the owner of the warehouse, your costs are going up.

Developing new math skills and solving different applications will require patience and effort. Use your own logical thinking skills to help you approach math challenges in a way that makes the most sense to you. There are usually many ways to tackle a math challenge. Linking to something you already know to help you discover something new is empowering. After doing this, many of my students have said, "I can do math!"

Discussion Prompts:
- Which format did you like the best – the short story, the big ideas, or the additional insights from the error analysis? Why?
- Did you go back and reread any portion of this chapter? Why or why not?
- When your math work is returned with comments, it is often better to leave your work as is and try again in another spot. Why?
- How do you compute profit?

Curious? Research Prompts:

- Greatest episodes on the TV show "Shark Tank"
- Functions
- Example of a graph of a cost and an income equation. Example of a graph showing profit over time.

Learning Task: *"The Story Behind the Cost and Income Equations"*

Nurture Your Growth Mindset By Engaging In This Short Activity

"*The Story Behind the Cost and Income Equations*"

Note that discussion is so important when exploring these activities. Discuss and compare your responses with peers or family members.

(You will need either graph paper or a graphing utility or program to complete this activity. If needed, graph paper is provided in Appendix B.)

1. Graph the cost equation provided in this chapter: C = $3,000x + $98,000

2. On the same axes, graph the income equation provided in this chapter: I = $5,000x

3. Determine the break-even point.

4. Explain what it means to be a break-even point.

5. Construct a different cost equation such that the break-even point will occur sooner than in the example in this chapter. Determine the new break-even point for your new example.

6. Construct a different cost equation such that the break-even point will occur later than in the example in this chapter. Determine the new break-even point for your new example.

Note: The activities at the end of each chapter can be used for peer discussion, class explorations, summer reading list participants, teen clubs, home schooling, or other. If needed, most of the answers can then be easily verified on-line. With technology, knowledge is at your fingertips. Practice your research skills. Personal choice or opinion answers will vary.

CHAPTER 5

WHY ARE SPATIAL RELATIONSHIPS IMPORTANT TO ME?

What if…you decided to host a drone competition in your warehouse to generate additional interest in the sport and additional income for you? To please both the drone operators and the spectators, you planned a racing circuit that includes technical challenge and high speed. You included a vertical hairpin turn followed by a long straight line. And when you tested this arrangement, you were very pleased. The speed on the straight line seemed even more impressive because of the greater acceleration after the slower hairpin turn. Now you need to add the finishing touches. You plan to include neon props from floor to ceiling. Glowing shapes, lines and angles will be everywhere.

 What are the big ideas wrapped up in this story?

- **Formulas**

The racing circuit area will be roped off with neon tube lighting. This area measures 100 feet by 50 feet. The total distance around the racing circuit area if you added the lengths of each side as you walked around the area is the perimeter of that area. How many feet of neon tube lighting will you need?

Adding up all the sides, you determine that you will need 300 feet of neon tube lighting. Or, a shorter way to express this equation is P = 2(length) + 2(width) because you have two sides of equal length and two sides of equal width in a rectangle. Like in this example, there is often more than one way to come to a solution.

For a rectangle, P = length + width + length + width
Or   P = 2(length) + 2(width)

In this example, P = 100 feet + 50 feet + 100 feet + 50 feet
Or   P = 2(100 feet) + 2(50 feet)

P = 300 feet

Interpret your solution: You will need 300 feet of neon tube lighting to rope off the perimeter of the racing circuit.

The warehouse measures 40 feet floor to ceiling. For safety reasons, the maximum height drones will be allowed to fly is 30 feet high. Safety nets will be suspended 10 feet below the ceiling. How can you determine how many safety nets you will need?

The area formula for a rectangular shape can be used to determine how many safety nets you will need.

For a rectangle, Area = (length)(width)

In this example, Area = (100 feet)(50 feet)
Area = 5,000 ft^2 or 5,000 square feet

Interpret your solution: You will need enough safety nets to cover an area of 5,000 ft^2.

Your entire racing circuit must fit inside the dimensions you have to work with. How can you determine the total amount of airspace? The total airspace for the racing circuit can be determined using the volume formula for a rectangular prism. This information will be needed when you advertise the event.

For a rectangular prism, Volume = (length)(width)(height)

In this example, Volume = (100 feet)(50 feet)(30 feet)
Volume = 150,000 ft³ or 150,000 cubic feet

Interpret your solution: Drone pilots will be flying within an airspace of 150,000 ft³.

Many students may have used one or more of these formulas in earlier grades. Here, the emphasis is in using them to visualize and design your racing circuit.

- **Shapes**

One of the neon props will be a right triangle. Drones must be able to fly through a right triangular prop that is suspended from the ceiling. One vertex of this right triangular prop will need to be 27 feet from the ceiling. The base of the right triangle will need to be ten feet from the floor and run parallel to the floor for a distance of four feet. Visualizing the right triangle prop suspended from the ceiling in this way, can you determine what the height of the prop will need to be?

Just to be sure, you checked the numbers. Recall that the warehouse measures 40 feet floor to ceiling. 27 feet + ? feet + 10 feet = 40 feet. The height of the right triangular prop will need to be three feet. 27 feet + 3 feet + 10 feet does equal 40 feet. It all checks out.

You are also planning to suspend four regular pentagon props in line with each other but spaced one foot apart. To make it look more interesting, you decide to rotate the position of each regular pentagon so that they are not all lined up in the same way. The first three regular pentagon props will be rotated approximately 30 degrees counterclockwise from the previous one. The fourth pentagon will be in the same position as the first pentagon. This will make a much more interesting line-up.

- **Pythagorean Theorem**

How can you determine the length of the third side of the right triangular prop? The Pythagorean Theorem can be used to determine the length of the third side of the right triangular prop that will be suspended from the ceiling. This information is also needed for your advertising. Drone pilots need to know that the wingspan of their drone will comfortably fit through the prop.

The Pythagorean Theorem states that $a^2 + b^2 = c^2$
(where "c" represents the longest side of the right triangle)

In this example, 3^2 feet $+ 4^2$ feet $= c^2$
$$9 \text{ feet} + 16 \text{ feet} = c^2$$
$$25 \text{ feet} = c^2$$
$$5 \text{ feet} = c$$

Interpret your solution: The length of the third side of the right triangular prop will be 5 feet. The diagonal width of the drone quadcopters that frequent your warehouse are typically less than 1.5 feet. Experienced drone pilots know that a diagonal width of less than two feet will allow for more safety and flexibility when maneuvering the drone through this prop.

There are also theorems about lines, angles, and parallelograms. Working with theorems helps you to develop logical thinking skills. Such skills are important in life and career.

You may have noticed that there is a lot of vocabulary specific to shapes and spatial relationships. Learn the vocabulary. Drawing pictures can be very helpful. Shapes and spatial relationships are less abstract than using variables to represent numbers. Visual learners or students who like to draw often like that. You may have also noted that solving equations are skills that are still needed when you explore shapes and spatial relationships. This is why mathematics is said to be a "cumulative" subject. It is similar to studying a new language. You would not be well prepared to enroll in Spanish 3 if you did not succeed in Spanish 1 and Spanish 2. You will need to remember and understand previous math skills to leap to the next math challenge.

 Error analysis.

Again, my own students have taught me so many things. What additional insights can you gain from these examples? Can you spot the errors before reading the explanations?

- **Incorrect**   Area = 5,000 ft   *Try again*

Why did you mark my answer as "Try again"? This student made an error with the units. The correct answer is Area $= 5,000$ ft^2. Units are very important. If your neighbor offered to pay you 40 to help him learn a new computer application, you should probably verify that it is forty dollars and not forty cents or forty oranges. This might seem like a silly example, but 5,000 ft and 5,000 ft^2 are not even close to the same thing. If you look more closely at the formula you use to compute the area of a rectangle, you will see that two dimensions are needed – length and width. A rectangle is a two dimensional (2-D) shape. This means it needs an answer with two dimensions. Feet times feet equals feet squared. Or, square feet can also be used.

Notice that the volume formula for a rectangular prism needs three dimensions – length, width, and height. A rectangular prism is three dimensional (3-D). Feet times feet times feet equals feet cubed or cubic feet. The volume of the race circuit airspace is 150,000 ft^3, or 150,000 cubic feet.

- **Incorrect**

$$40 \text{ feet total height} - 10 \text{ feet from floor} =$$
$$30 \text{ feet left}$$

$$30 \text{ feet} - 27 \text{ feet from ceiling} =$$
$$4 \text{ feet left}$$

The height of the right triangular prop will be 4 feet. *Try again*

But I reasoned it all out. How can it be wrong? This student made a simple computation error, which is so easy to do, especially if you are distracted. Make a habit of checking your work. In this case, for example, 27 feet + 4 feet + 10 feet does not equal 40 feet. Checking your work to see if your answer is reasonable usually takes only a few seconds. Redoing all the work usually takes much longer.

- **Incorrect**

$$3^2 + 4^2 = c^2$$
$$6 + 8 = c^2 \quad \textit{Try again}$$
$$14 = c^2$$
$$\sqrt{14} = c$$

Why do I need to do it again? I showed all my work. This student set up the equation correctly, but there is an error in the second line of work. When you write 3^2 this means three times three. It does not mean three plus three. And 4^2 means four times four. It does not mean four plus four.

- **Incorrect**
  (Two errors)

$$3^2 + b^2 = 4^2 \quad \textit{Try again}$$
$$9 + b^2 = 16$$
$$b^2 = 16\text{-}7$$

$$b^2 = 7 \qquad \textit{Keep going}$$

(This student still has not solved for b.)

I did put the largest number in for c. Why is it wrong? This student plugged in the values incorrectly. When you use the Pythagorean Theorem, the "c" does represent the longest side of the right triangle. It is called the hypotenuse of the right triangle. And yes, four is larger than three but you don't even know the length of the third side yet. In a right triangle, the third side in this example must be five. Note that five is larger than both three and four. When you apply the Pythagorean Theorem, "c" must be the hypotenuse, the longest side of the right triangle. The hypotenuse is opposite the right angle.

Also, this student did not solve for "b". This student solved for "b²". There is still more work to do. If you needed an exact answer, you would need to take the square root of both sides of the equation. If b^2 equals seven, then $b = \sqrt{7}$.

Note that seven is not a perfect square. A whole number multiplied by itself will not equal seven. Twenty-five is a perfect square because five times five equals twenty-five. If you only needed an approximate answer, you could use a calculator to find the approximation for the square root of seven.

Another way of expressing $\sqrt{7}$ is seven raised to the ½ power, or $7^{1/2}$. The exponent in this example is the fraction ½. The number ½ is a rational number because it can be written as a fraction and the denominator is not zero. Therefore, the exponent in this example is called a rational exponent.

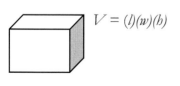 $V = (l)(w)(h)$

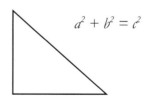 $a^2 + b^2 = c^2$

Discussion Prompts:

- How would you advertise for your drone racing competition? What information would be important in your advertising?

- Would the formulas for perimeter, area and volume of the drone racing airspace be different if the airspace was the shape of a cube (the length = the width = the height) instead of a rectangular shape? Why or why not? Would the units be different? Why or why not?

- In life, when would you need exact answers? And when would estimates be sufficient? Can you think of several examples of each?

Curious? Research Prompts:

- Math vocabulary is very precise. What is the difference between a "regular pentagon" and a "pentagon"? Is a regular pentagon also a pentagon? Is a pentagon also a regular pentagon? Is it possible to have a "regular rectangle"? Why or why not? If yes, what are you more likely to call it? If not, why?

- What are Pythagorean Triples? Why are they important?

- What is the sum of the interior angles of any triangle? If you created a rectangle by sketching two triangles side by side, what would the sum of the interior angles be? How do you know?

Learning Task: *"Exploring Geometric Shapes"*

Nurture Your Growth Mindset By Engaging In This Short Activity

"Exploring Geometric Shapes"

Note that discussion is so important when exploring these activities. Discuss or compare your responses with peers or family members.

(You will need a protractor for this activity. Also, if needed, graph paper is provided in Appendix B.)

1. Sketch accurate representations of at least five geometric shapes. Name the shapes.

2. Measure and label any angles that are contained in those shapes.

3. Pick any three of these shapes and enlarge them without changing the angle measurements.

4. Explain the difference between the geometric terms "similarity" and "congruency".

5. Distort these shapes by changing some angle measurement(s) and connect them to design a cartoon character – just for fun.

Note: The activities at the end of each chapter can be used for peer discussion, class explorations, summer reading list participants, teen clubs, home schooling, or other. If needed, most of the answers can then be easily verified on-line. With technology, knowledge is at your fingertips. Practice your research skills. Personal choice or opinion answers will vary.

CHAPTER 6

WHAT ELSE CAN MODELING DO FOR ME?

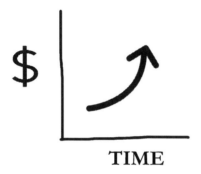

TIME

You opened your business three years ago, but your business is still not making a profit. Your business has not even reached the break-even point yet. You will break even when your total costs equal your total income. Unfortunately, your total costs still exceed your total income. Mathematically, we say C > I. This is making you nervous. It is time to relook at your savings. Will your savings last long enough? Will you have enough to live on and to cover your business expenses until you start making a profit?

An exponential function models the amount of savings you will have based on the interest rate you are earning on your money. You are earning interest on your savings and you are earning interest on your interest. To lessen your worries, it would be helpful to know how much money you will accumulate over the next 24 months.

What are the big ideas wrapped up in this story?

- **Exponential Functions**

The banking industry could not exist as it does today without exponential functions. The formula $A = P(e^{rt})$ is an example of an exponential function. The "e" in this exponential function is a very special number just like "π". Like pi, it is very useful in many applications. These numbers are so useful, in fact, that both of these numbers can be found on a scientific calculator. The value of "e" rounded to three decimal places is 2.718. This exponential function, $A = P(e^{rt})$, models the amount of money you will accumulate over time when your interest is compounded continuously. This is an example of exponential growth. Remember, you are continuously earning interest on your interest.

Let's summarize what each variable represents:

A = the amount of money you accumulated
P = the original amount of money you started with
r = interest rate, expressed in decimal form
t = the amount of time your money is invested

Currently, all your bills are paid in full and you even put enough money on your debit card to pay your business expenses and your living expenses for the next 12 months. After doing that, you put the rest of your savings in an account that earns a higher interest rate. You currently have $50,000 in this account. If you did not withdraw any money from this account for the next 12 months, how much money will you accumulate in the next 12 months? The interest rate is 3% per year compounded continuously. Written as a decimal value, the rate is 0.03. Because the interest rate is "per year", the 12 months is converted to 1 year.

Plugging in the known values, we have

$$A = 50{,}000(e^{(.03)(1)})$$
$$A = 50{,}000(2.718^{(.03)(1)})$$
$$A = \$51{,}522 \text{ (rounded to nearest dollar)}$$

Interpret your solution: The accumulated value is approximately $51,522. This means that in 12 months your money has earned you an additional $1,522.

Recall that in the exponential growth model, you earn interest on more than just the original dollar amount of $50,000. You continuously earn interest on your interest. This additional money will certainly help.

- **Comparing an Exponential Function with a Linear Function**

Fortunately, none of your expenses have had price increases since you opened your business. Your total costs keep increasing by the same amount each month. Another way of saying this is to say that the rate of change for your total cost function is the same amount each month. Your cost function is an increasing linear function. Your total costs increase by the same amount each month. As shown in the example above, your savings will also keep increasing each month if you do not withdraw any money. However, in the exponential function the amount of increase each month is not the same amount each month. This is an example of exponential growth. Exponential growth functions increase much more rapidly than increasing linear functions. Graphs of exponential growth functions look very different than graphs of increasing linear functions. This is because the rate of change in an exponential function is not constant.

 Error analysis.

In all the math classes I have ever taught, my own students have taught me so many things. Don't be afraid to ask questions. Clearing up your questions as soon as possible will lessen frustration and help you to succeed.

- **Incorrect** $\quad\quad A = 50,000(e^{(3)(1)})$ *Try again*

$A = 50,000(2.718^{(3/\text{year})(1\ \text{year})})$

$A = 50,000(20.079)$

$A = \$1,003,950$ *Does this seem reasonable?*

How can it be wrong? I followed the formula. This student did so many things correctly. They are using the correct formula, plugging in values in the appropriate spots, and even doing the computations correctly (multiplication and raising to a power). The error is forgetting to compute the decimal value of 3%. The formula is not written to plug the rate in as a percent. The formula is written to plug in the rate as a decimal value. Before doing all the work for any formula, be sure to know what the variables represent and in what format they need to be.

Units can also help you if you are uncomfortable with a formula or you just don't know what operation(s) to do. Check out the example below. Recall that the amount of money you accumulated is represented by "A" in this formula. "A" is an amount of money (expressed in dollars); therefore, all of the units on the other side of the equation must boil down to dollars so that we have dollars = dollars. The number "e" has no units.

$$\text{dollars} = \text{dollars}(2.718^{(.03/\text{year})(1\ \text{year})})$$

If you look at the multiplication in the power that the number "e" (rounded to 2.718) is raised to more closely, you will see that the "year" units cancel.

$$\left(\frac{.03}{\text{year}}\right)\left(\frac{1\ \text{year}}{1}\right) = .03\ \text{(with no units attached)}$$

Note that $\frac{year}{year}$ reduces to one just like $\frac{4}{4}$ reduces to one. Multiplying by one does not change what you already have. So, it all checks out. The only remaining units are dollars = dollars.

A lot of simple errors can be avoided by paying attention to units and using them to help you. You might tackle a math challenge that requires five or more math steps and the only error is a simple unit error that causes your final answer to be incorrect. Of course, after reading this book you will be on high alert and you will avoid many of those types of errors.

Let's look at the student's error again in terms of reasonableness. It is unreasonable to expect $50,000 to grow to over 1 million dollars invested for only one year at a 3% (written as a decimal .03) interest rate. If your interest rate was 100% (or 1.0 if written as a decimal), you would have

$$A = 50,000(2.718)^{(1.0)(1)}$$
$$A = \$135,900$$

One hundred percent is so much larger than 3% and yet this dollar amount, $135,900 is not even close to the amount computed above when the interest rate was only 3% ($1,003,950). Checking to see if an answer is reasonable can help you find and fix errors.

Discussion Prompts:
- Percent means "out of 100". How can this help you to remember how to convert 5%, for example, to a decimal value?
- Can you use units to help you figure out if you should divide or multiply in the following example? A drone maintains a speed of 164 miles per hour on a straight path for 3 minutes. Three minutes is equivalent to 0.05 hours. How many miles did it travel? Should you multiply or divide 164 by .05? Why?
- One mile per hour is approximately equal to 1.6 kilometer per hours. Expressed as a ratio we have $\frac{1 \text{ mile}}{1.6 \text{ kilometers}}$ or $\frac{1.6 \text{ kilometers}}{1 \text{ mile}}$. Using units

to help you, which version of this ratio would you multiply by to convert 164 miles to kilometers (per hour)? Will this give you the units you want?

Curious? Research Prompts:

- Exponential functions
- What is a unit price? How can you find a unit price? How can unit prices help you save money at the grocery store?
- Famous costly math mistakes
- Using units to understand and solve more math problems

Learning Task: *"Exploring Exponential Functions"*

Nurture Your Growth Mindset By Engaging
In This Short Activity

"Exploring Exponential Functions"

Note that discussion is so important when exploring these activities. Discuss or compare your responses with peers or family members.

(You will need either graph paper or a graphing utility or program to complete this activity. If needed, graph paper is provided in Appendix B.)

1. Suppose the news commentator said, "Gasoline prices have increased exponentially." Explain what the news commentator is trying to convey.

2. Let the x value represent the month. Let the y value represent the cost of the gasoline for that month. Identify at least ten coordinates that might appear on an exponential curve representing the gas prices with respect to time.

3. Plot the data points you provided in step 2.

4. Does your graph depict an exponential growth curve? Why or why not?

5. If your graph does not look like a typical exponential growth curve, what data do you need to change so that it looks like a typical exponential growth curve? Change your coordinates and redo your graph if needed.

Note: The activities at the end of each chapter can be used for peer discussion, class explorations, summer reading list participants, teen clubs, home schooling, or other. If needed, most of the answers can then be easily verified on-line. With technology, knowledge is at your fingertips. Practice your research skills. Personal choice or opinion answers will vary.

CHAPTER 7

CAN THE STATS HELP ME MAKE AN INFORMED DECISION?

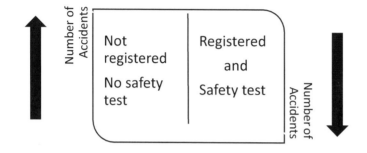

Interest in drone racing as a sport is growing locally and nationally. You have already hosted four drone racing competitions. The publicity has been amazing. Although these events require a lot of overtime, the additional monthly income is nice. Also, memberships have nearly doubled since you opened. Your monthly income has increased. Fortunately, your monthly costs have not increased. This will help you reach the break-even point sooner.

All of this is good news for you and your business. However, something terrible happened during the last drone racing event. One of the drones malfunctioned, broke through the safety netting, and nearly collided with a spectator. The spectator was rattled but fortunately not hurt. You were even more rattled than the spectator. To think of what could have happened. This scare has prompted you to re-examine your accident insurance.

What are the big ideas wrapped up in this story?

- **Using statistics to make a decision**

For the purpose of this story, imagine the following. Your insurance agent claims that according to the Amateur Sports Industry, the chances of having a major accident in your warehouse that requires emergency medical care is very high if the drone operators are not registered and have not passed a safety test. Statistics indicate that fifty-seven percent* of amateur drone pilots will be involved in an accident that will require emergency care for themselves or a spectator(s). If the amateur drone pilots are required to register their drones and to pass The Recreational UAS Safety Test (TRUST), this percentage drops to only seven percent*. To minimize your liability, such statistics would indicate that drone registration and proof of test passage for the drone operator must be required to practice or compete in your warehouse.

Your insurance agent also explains that the Amateur Sports Industry offers both a high-deductible insurance policy and a low-deductible insurance policy. A high-deductible policy has a lower cost, but the insurance does not kick in until you have personally paid out a higher dollar amount. A low-deductible policy has a higher cost, but you will not have to personally pay out as much before the insurance kicks in. Which option is better for you?

After additional discussion with your insurance agent, you have decided to purchase the high-deductible policy with the lower cost. Although the insurance does not kick in until you have paid out a higher dollar amount out of your pocket, drone registration and the requirement for drone pilots to pass TRUST greatly decreases the probability of accidents requiring emergency care. This is what you will need to do. After you break-even, you will reevaluate your accident insurance again. For now, the lower cost policy is the way to go.

Discussion prompts:
- When you purchase your first car, what statistics would you want to know?

- Drones can vary in size and weight. For recreational drone racing, should your warehouse provide maximum size and weight restrictions? Why or why not? Minimum size and weight restrictions? Why or why not? Speed restrictions? Why or why not?
- If you decided to post size, weight, and speed restrictions how would you efficiently monitor all of this?

Curious? Research prompts:
- TRUST – test for recreational drone pilots
- Drone statistics – commercial, military, and recreation
- FAA rules and regulations for drone hobbyists

Learning Task: *"Using Statistics"*

*Statistics are not available for this very specific scenario that presumably takes place over ten years in the future. Stated values were created to suit the purpose of this story.

Nurture Your Growth Mindset By Engaging In This Short Activity

"Using Statistics"

Note that discussion is so important when exploring these activities. Discuss or compare your responses with peers or family members.

1. Suppose that 650 drone hobbyists visited your warehouse last year to either practice their racing skills or to compete. Also suppose that you did not verify any drone registrations and you did not verify that the drone operators had passed the safety test called TRUST. If fifty-seven percent of these drone pilots will be involved in an accident that requires emergency medical care, how many drone pilots will be involved in such accidents?

2. How can you quickly determine whether your answer is reasonable or not?

3. Recall that the statistic drops substantially if you verify the above requirements. How many drone pilots are likely to be involved in such accidents if the percentage drops to seven percent?

4. How can you quickly determine whether your answer is reasonable or not?

5. Explain why it appears to be a wise decision to verify and document registration and passage of safety tests for accident insurance reasons. Make up realistic numbers that support your argument such as the costs involved to do all the verifications versus the costs that you would need to pay out on your high deductible policy before your insurance kicks in.

Note: The activities at the end of each chapter can be used for peer discussion, class explorations, summer reading list participants, teen clubs, home schooling, or other. If needed, most of the answers can then be easily verified on-line. With technology, knowledge is at your fingertips. Practice your research skills. Personal choice or opinion answers will vary.

CHAPTER 8

EVERYTHING IS ALWAYS CHANGING. HOW CAN I MODEL THAT?

unsplash.com

Conversations with your insurance agent has prompted you to find a better way to monitor and document the maximum speed of each drone as the pilots practice or compete in your warehouse. The survival of your business depends on it – even if only one accident occurs in your warehouse any time soon.

 What are the big ideas wrapped up in this story?

- **Limitations of a simple formula to model the real world**

You remember a simple formula where distance will equal the rate (speed you are traveling) multiplied by the time interval you traveled.

$$\text{distance} = (\text{rate})(\text{time})$$
$$d = rt$$

If you wanted to rearrange this formula to find the rate, you simply divide both sides of the equation by time.

$$d = rt$$

$$\frac{d}{t} = \frac{rt}{t} \quad \textit{Do you remember what happens with } \frac{t}{t} \, ?$$

$$\frac{d}{t} = r$$

Great effort and good work, but then you realize that this formula will not do what you need it to do. This formula only works if the rate (or speed) is constant. The drones are not flying at the same speed throughout their flight.

- **Comparing or contrasting formulas**

You need a different formula. After some research, you found another formula that computes an average velocity. Speed and velocity are both rates of change. Speed describes how fast an object is moving. Velocity also describes how fast an object is moving but it also describes the direction the object is moving. For example, a car may be traveling at 65 miles per hour on a highway traveling south. The speed is 65 miles per hour. The velocity is 65 miles per hour south.

The formula looks complicated. But you remembered what a math teacher once told you. If you understand what the quantities are in the formula, plug them in correctly, and compute correctly, you can do this. After reading and rereading and looking at examples you figured it out.

$$\text{Average velocity} = \frac{f(b) - f(a)}{b - a}$$

This formula uses function notation in the numerator, the top part of the fraction on the right.

During competition, drones fly the fastest when they are racing on a straight horizontal path. The notation *f(a)* represents the position of the drone at the start of the straight horizontal path. The notation *f(b)* represents the position of the drone at the end of the straight horizontal path. In the denominator of the fraction, the letter *a* represents the time when the drone begins to travel along the straightaway. The letter *b* represents the time when the drone finishes the straightaway. The straightaway runs the width of the racing circuit from the 20 foot mark to the 80 foot mark and runs east to west. A drone reaches the 20 foot mark on the straightaway 15 seconds after starting the racing circuit. Sixteen seconds after starting the racing circuit the drone reaches the 80 foot mark. To compute the average velocity of this drone, we pop this information into the formula as follows.

$$\text{Average velocity} = \frac{80 \text{ feet} - 20 \text{ feet}}{16 \text{ seconds} - 15 \text{ seconds}} \text{ west}$$

$$\text{Average velocity} = \frac{60 \text{ feet}}{1 \text{ sec}} \text{ west}$$

$$\text{Average velocity} = 60 \text{ feet per second - heading west}$$

Interpret your solution: The average velocity of the drone during its flight on the straightaway is 60 feet per second (or, approximately 40.9 miles per hour) – heading west.

Again, good effort. But the average velocity still does not tell you the maximum velocity of the drone during its flight along the straightaway heading west. For example, the average of 20 mph, 42 mph, and 60 mph would be approximately 41 mph. But the maximum velocity in this example would be 60 mph west. The maximum velocity is nineteen miles per hour faster than the average velocity. Remember, it is the maximum velocity that is important for accident insurance purposes. An average will not work for your needs.

- **Calculus is the mathematics of change**

There must be another way to figure this out. You stumbled on something called a "derivative" that computes "an instantaneous rate of change". You read that the derivative of a function describes the function's instantaneous rate of change at a certain point. But you were interrupted when a friend stopped by. Your friend works in law enforcement and had a great idea. You need to purchase a laser velocimeter, similar to what law enforcement uses to determine the velocity of cars. This device can measure velocity at a precise moment in time. A snapshot of the rate of change at a precise moment.

Your growth mindset is doing great if you made it this far. You are crushing it! This is the beginning of Calculus. Although you were physically and mentally exhausted at this point, it was never clearer to you than it is now. Mathematics is the language of technology and you better get on board.

Discussion prompts:

- Function notation explicitly tells you what to plug into that function. If the function is called "f(x)" and is written f(x) = 2x + 1. What do you think f(3) is trying to tell you to do?
- Can you think of example(s) where it is useful to use d = (r)(t)? Can you think of other examples where it is helpful to know the average rate of change (as shown in the average velocity formula above)?
- Velocity is an example of a rate of change. How fast your ice cream melts is another example of a rate of change. Can you think of other examples?

Curious? Research prompts:

- Order of operations with fractions. Order of operations for complex (or stacked) fractions.
- The physics of how drones fly
- Velocimeter

Learning Task: *"Using Units To Help You"*

Nurture Your Growth Mindset By Engaging
In This Short Activity

"Using Units To Help You"

Note that discussion is so important when exploring these activities. Discuss or compare your results with peers or family members.

1. Using only units and known ratios, such as $\frac{60 \text{ seconds}}{1 \text{ minute}}$, show how to convert 60 feet per second to approximately 40.9 miles per hour.

2. Law enforcement was stationed at two points along a highway running north to south fifteen miles apart. The posted speed limit is 65 miles per hour. A car was clocked at the north point at 65 mph. At the southern point, the same car was clocked at 60 mph 11.5 minutes later. Sketch a visual of this scenario.

3. With the given information, can you determine if the car exceeded the posted speed limit at any point during this time frame? Explain. Include examples and show your work to justify your response.

Note: The activities at the end of each chapter can be used for peer discussion, class explorations, summer reading list participants, teen clubs, home schooling, or other. If needed, most of the answers can then be easily verified on-line. With technology, knowledge is at your fingertips. Practice your research skills. Personal choice or opinion answers will vary.

CHAPTER 9

THE BEGINNING

Your initiative to read "Crush Math Anxiety With Drones, Succeed In Math By Nurturing A Growth Mindset Through Drone Stories" is the beginning of a growth mindset that will help you to succeed in high school math. Questioning, discussing, and referencing the content of this book will help you absorb these big ideas and nurture a growth mindset. Congratulations on taking this first step.

The topics in this book represent some of the big ideas in Algebra, Geometry, Statistics, Precalculus, and even Calculus. Understanding some of these big ideas can help you to link information that you already know to new information. These big ideas also highlight the cumulative nature of mathematics and its ultimate power to model the real world. Math isn't just numbers and computations staring at you from a screen or scribbled on a piece of paper. When you understand the big ideas and how they are applied, you learn that math tells a story. And as your math skills grow, the story becomes more and more interesting. Keep at it and enjoy the story.

Math anxiety – you crushed it with drones!

This isn't the end, it's just the beginning of a new growth mindset that will help you succeed.

ENDNOTES

Chapter 1

[1]Boaler, Jo. "Everyone Can Learn Mathematics to High Levels: The Evidence from Neuroscience that Should Change our Teaching." American Mathematical Society, 1 February 2019, blogs.AMS.org/matheducation/2019/02.

[2]Boaler, Jo. "Everyone Can Learn Mathematics to High Levels: The Evidence from Neuroscience that Should Change our Teaching." American Mathematical Society, 1 February 2019, blogs.AMS.org/matheducation/2019/02.

[3]Vos Savant, Marilyn and Fleischer, Leonore. "Brain Building In Just 12 Weeks." Bantam Books, 1991. Page 64.

[4]Boaler, Jo. "Mathematical Mindsets, Unleashing Students' Potential Through Creative Math, Inspiring Messages and Innovative Teaching." Jossey-Bass, 2016. Page 31.

[5]Saul, Mark et al. "Mathematics: Gatekeeper or Gateway?" American Mathematical Society, 2 February 2019, blogs.AMS.org/matheducation/2019/02.

[6]Lynch, Matthew. "How STEM Education Can Help End Poverty." Pedagogue, 15 January 2018, https://www.thetechedvocate.org/stem-education-can-help-end-poverty/.

[7]Sharma, Akshay. "13 Reasons Why Math Is Important." LifeHacks, https://lifehacks.io/reasons-why-math-is-important/.

[8]Lynch, Matthew. "How STEM Education Can Help End Poverty." Pedagogue, 15 January 2018, https://www.thetechedvocate.org/stem-education-can-help-end-poverty/.

[9]Marr, Bernard. "The 10 Vital Skills You Will Need For the Future of Work." Forbes, 29 April 2019, https://www.forbes.com/sites/bernardmarr/2019/04/29/the-10-vital-skills-you-will-need-for-the-future-of-work/

Chapter 2

[1]Vuleta, Branka, "33+ Electrifying Drone Statistics [2021 Edition]". SeedScientific, 11 February 2021, https://seedscientific.com/drone-statistics/#respond.

[2]Vuleta, Branka, "33+ Electrifying Drone Statistics [2021 Edition]". SeedScientific, 11 February 2021, https://seedscientific.com/drone-statistics/#respond.

[3]University of North Dakota, Programs, www.und.edu/programs/index.html.

[4]Krypto Labs. "Drone X Challenge." https://dronexchallenge2020.com/.

[5]Drobots Company. "National Aerial Robotics League Drone Competition For Schools And Clubs." https://drobotscompany.com/drone-stem-competition-grades-1-12-high-school-kids-teens/.

[6]CNN Business. "CVS just delivered its first prescriptions via drones." Video/Business, 6 November 2019, https://www.cnn.com/videos/business/2019/11/06/ups-cvs-drone-delivery-prescription-orig.cnn-business.

[7]Kruk, Brittany. "During Covid-19, drone delivery is really taking off." Walgreens Boots Alliance, 11 May 2020, https://www.walgreensbootsalliance.com/news-media/our-stories/during-covid-19-drone-delivery-is-really-taking-off

[8]Federal Aviation Administration. "Drone Response Playbook For Public Safety." September 2020, https://www.faa.gov/uas/public_safety_gov/public_safety_toolkit/media/Public_Safety_Drone_Playbook.pdf.

[9]McFarland, Matt. "Amazon's delivery drones may drop packages via drones." CNN Business, 14 February 2017, https://money.cnn.com/2017/02/14/technology/amazon-drone-patent/index.html.

[10]McFarland, Matt. "Amazon's delivery drones may drop packages via drones." CNN Business, 14 February 2017, https://money.cnn.com/2017/02/14/technology/amazon-drone-patent/index.html.

[11]Lillicrap, Simon. "28Million Fans, £100,000 prizes, Welcome To The Crazy World of Elite Drone Racing." The Sportsman, 21 December 2020, https://www.thesportsman.com/features/28million-fans-100-000-prizes-welcome-to-the-crazy-world-of-elite-drone-racing

[12]Stephenson, Kristen. "The Drone Racing League sets quadcopter speed record." Guinness World Records, 20 July 2017, https://www.guinnessworldrecords.com/news/2017/7/the-drone-racing-league-builds-the-worlds-fastest-racing-drone-482701/.

[13]Slider, James. "Fly These 6 Exhilarating Drone Racing Worlds in The Drone Racing League Simulator." 28 September 2020, https://news.xbox.com/en-us/2020/09/28/exhilarating-drone-racing-worlds/.

[14]Techeblog. "World's Largest Drone Display Consisted of 3,051 Unmanned Aerial Vehicles." 10 November 2020,

https://www.techeblog.com/largest-drone-display-china-guinness-world-records/.

Chapter 3

[1]Vos Savant, Marilyn and Fleischer, Leonore. "Brain Building In Just 12 Weeks." Bantam Books, 1991. Page 15.

BIBLIOGRAPHY

Boaler, Jo. *Limitless Mind: Learn, Lead and Live without Barriers.* HarperCollins, 2019.

Boaler, Jo. *Mathematical Mindsets: Unleashing Students' Potential through Creative Math, Inspiring Messages and Innovative Teaching 1ˢᵗ Edition.* Jossey-Bass, 2016.

Dormehl, Luke. "The history of drones in 10 milestones." Emerging Tech, 11 September 2018.

Dweck, Carol. *Mindset: The New Psychology of Success.* Random House, 2016.

Juniper, Adam. *The Complete Guide to Drones 2ⁿᵈ Edition.* Wellfleet Press, 2018.

Lujan, Michael L et al. "Common Core Standards and Strategies Flip Chart". National Governors Association Center for Best Practices and Council of Chief State School Officers, 2010.

Vos Savant, Marilyn and Fleischer, Leonore. *Brain Building In Just 12 Weeks.* Bantam Books, 1991.

GLOSSARY
(Working definitions relevant to this book)

Acceleration	The rate of change of the velocity of an object with respect to time
Algebra	The part of mathematics in which letters and other symbols are used to represent numbers and quantities in equations and formulas
Analysis	Detailed examination of something, typically as a basis for discussion or interpretation
Area	The measurement of a surface
Break-even point	The point at which income is equal to expenses
Calculus	The mathematical study of continuous change
Cost equation	The formula that represents all the costs for operating your business
Counterclockwise	Rotate in the opposite direction to the hands of a clock
Cumulative subject	An area of knowledge which expands as new facts or data is considered
Degree	A measure for angles
Dependent variable	The variable whose value will change depending on the value of another variable (referred to as the independent variable)
Diagonal	A straight line connecting opposite corners

Drone	Any unpiloted aircraft
Equation	A mathematical statement that asserts the equality of two expressions
Error analysis	A process of reviewing a solution and then looking for patterns of misunderstanding. Errors in mathematics can be factual, procedural, or conceptual. Errors may occur for a number of reasons. Reasons may include gaps in knowledge, misinformation, distractions that cause computation errors, misunderstanding the question, the vocabulary or the symbols, or even lack of practice.
Evaluate	Assess; form an idea about the number or value of something
Exponential equation	An equation containing a variable in the exponent
FAA	The Federal Aviation Administration is the largest transportation agency in the United States
Face	Any of the individual flat surfaces of a solid object
Formula	A mathematical relationship or rule expressed in symbols
Function	A special relationship such that each input has one and only one output
Function notation	A way to write functions that is easy to read and understand. The independent variable is commonly x and the dependent variable is f(x)

Geometry	The branch of mathematics concerned with the properties and relations of points, lines, surfaces, and solids
Graph	A picture or diagram that represents data or values in an organized manner
Growth mindset	The belief that a person's most basic abilities can be developed through dedication, hard work and practice
Horizontal line	A line which has a zero slope value and all points on the line have the same y value
Hypotenuse	The longest side of a right-angled triangle
Income equation	The formula that represents all the income for your business
Independent variable	A variable whose variation does not depend on that of another
Linear equation	An equation that makes a straight line when it is graphed. There are three forms of a linear equation: $y = mx + b$; $y - y_1 = m(x - x_1)$; $Ax + By = C$.
Magnitude	The size or extent of the number
Mars rover	A motor vehicle that travels across the surface of the planet Mars upon arrival

Math anxiety	Feeling uncomfortable or stressed about one's ability to do mathematics
Mathematical Modeling	The process of applying mathematics to a real world problem to make sense of the problem and identify a solution
Microcontroller	A small computer on a single metal-oxide-semiconductor (MOS) integrated circuit (IC) chip
Neuroscience	The scientific study of the nervous system. It is a multidisciplinary science that combines physiology, anatomy, molecular biology, developmental biology, cytology, computer science, and mathematical modeling
Optimization	The action of making the best or most effective use of a situation or resource
Parallel	Side by side and having the same distance continuously between them
Parallelogram	A simple quadrilateral with two pairs of parallel sides
Patent	A government authority or license conferring a right or title for a set period, especially the sole right to exclude others from making, using, or selling an invention
Pentagon	A plane figure with five straight sides and five angles
Perfect square	The product of a rational number multiplied by itself

Perimeter	The total distance if you walked around a 2-D shape. The length of a closed line bounding a plane area
Physics	The science of matter and energy and the interactions between the two
Plane	A flat surface with no thickness
Power	The use of an exponent to show how many times to use a number in a multiplication
Precalculus	A course in mathematics that prepares a student for Calculus
Profit	The money you make by running your business after all expenses are paid. A financial gain, especially the difference between the amount earned and the amount spent in buying, operating, or producing something
Pythagorean Theorem	A formal truth that describes the relationship between the three sides of a right triangle. Often shown as $a^2 + b^2 = c^2$ where "c" is the side opposite the right angle in a right triangle.
Ratio	The quantitative relation between two amounts showing the number of times one value contains or is contained within the other
Rational number	A number capable of being expressed as an integer or as a quotient (fraction) of integers, as long as the denominator of the fraction is not zero
Rectangular prism	A solid (3-dimensional) object which has six faces that are rectangles

Regular pentagon	A five-sided figure in which the angles are all equal and the sides are all equal
Right triangle	A triangle with a right angle (a 90 degree angle)
Rotor	A rotating assembly that provides the lift for a helicopter or other rotary-wing aircraft
Social sciences	The study of human society and of individual relationships within the society. Includes sociology, psychology, anthropology, economics, political science, and history.
Solve	To find a value (or values) we can put in place of a variable that makes the equation true
Spatial relationships	The relationships of objects in space with respect to each other or to ourselves
Square root	A number that when multiplied by itself equals a given number
Statistics	The mathematics of the collection, organization and interpretation of numerical data
STEAM	A philosophy of education for science, technology, engineering, the arts and mathematics that embraces teaching skills and subjects in a way that resembles real life
STEM	A philosophy of education for science, technology, engineering and mathematics that embraces teaching skills and subjects in a way that resembles real life

Synchronization	The operation or activity of two or more things at the same time or rate
Theorem	A truth that is not obvious but has been proved by a chain of logical reasoning or other accepted truths
Three dimensional (3-D)	Having or appearing to have length, width and depth
Two dimensional (2-D)	Having or appearing to have length and width
U.S. Patent and Trademark Office	The federal agency for granting U.S. patents and registering trademarks
Variable	A letter that expresses a numerical value or a number
Velocity	The speed of something in a given direction
Vertex	A part of a shape at which two or more line segments meet
Volume	The amount of space that a substance or object occupies, or that is enclosed within a container

APPENDIX A
Jo Boaler's Growth Mindset Suggestions For Math

In "Mathematical Mindsets, Unleashing Students' Potential Through Creative Math, Inspiring Messages, and Innovative Teaching, Dr. Jo Boaler concludes that the five recommendations listed below serve to open mathematical tasks and increase their potential for learning.

1. Open up the task so that there are multiple methods, pathways, and representations.

2. Include inquiry opportunities.

3. Ask the problem before teaching the method.

4. Add a visual component and ask students how they see the mathematics.

5. Extend the task to make it lower floor and higher ceiling.

6. Ask students to convince and reason; be skeptical.

APPENDIX B

Graph Paper

Title:

Use the space below for notes or calculations, if needed.

Title:

Use the space below for notes or calculations, if needed.

Title:

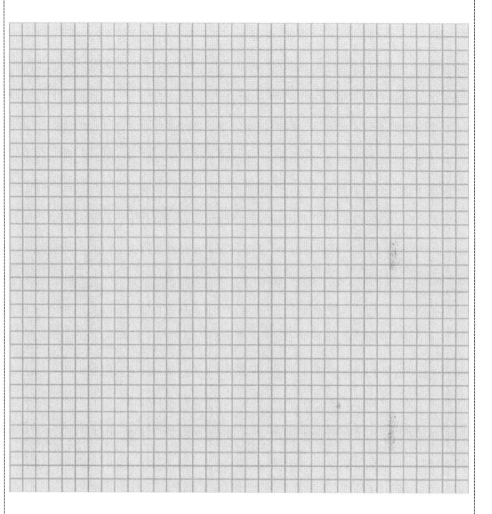

Use the space below for notes or calculations, if needed.

Title:

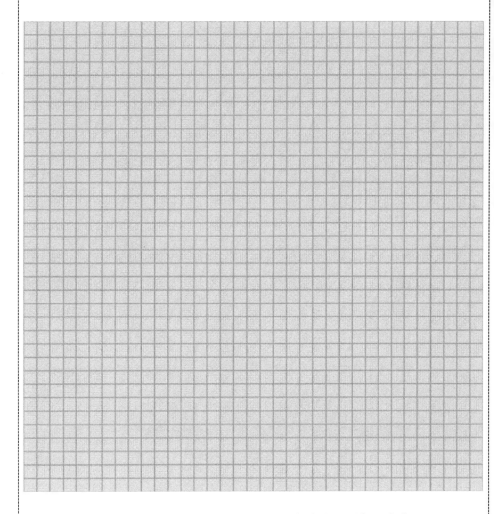

Use the space below for notes or calculations, if needed.

Title:

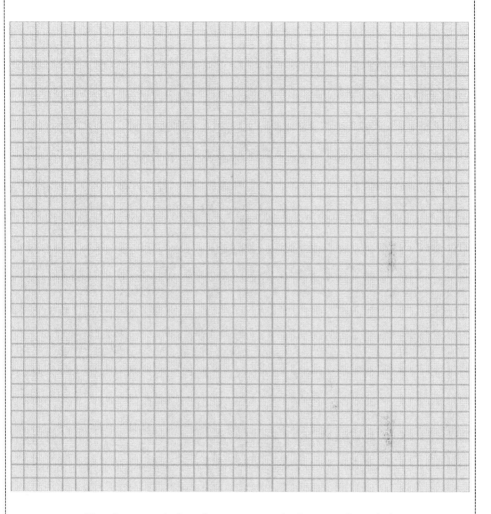

Use the space below for notes or calculations, if needed.

Title:

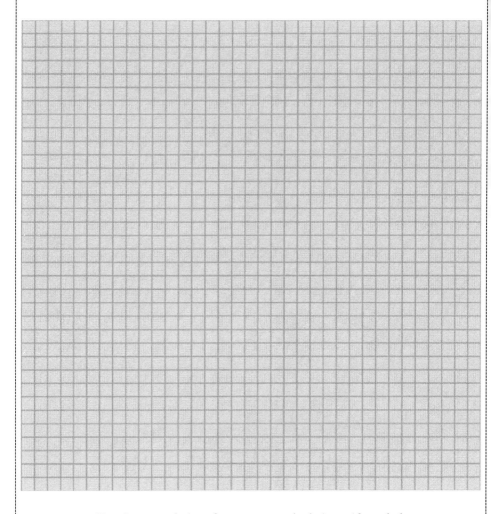

Use the space below for notes or calculations, if needed.

APPENDIX C
Common Core State Standards

The CCSS were created in 2009. These standards were designed to help educators plan purposeful instruction to promote student achievement. The expectations inherent in the standards were designed to be high yet attainable. The intent of these standards is to help students to be competitive internationally and to prepare them for life and careers in the 21st century.

Initially 46 states adopted the Common Core State Standards. However, education is often in flux. Some states have begun or passed legislation to repeal the standards. Change such as this can cause frustration and confusion, but debate between knowledgeable participants can be a very positive thing. Debate can foster positive improvements, perhaps especially on local levels with extenuating circumstances.

Regardless of your point of view, technology demands a citizenship and workforce with increased math knowledge and skills. One aim of this book is to help students make math connections to real world examples that interest them. This book also serves as a refresher and review. Throughout this book, grade 7 and grade 8 expectations are linked with the high school expectations. Don't get caught with outdated math skills. To build a comfortable life and career in the 21st century, advances in technology will not wait for you to catch up.

For those who want to join the debate from either stance, additional information about middle school and high school mathematics Common Core Standards (CCSS was later shortened to CCS) is provided below. The CCS for high school mathematics provide detailed expectations in the following areas: number and quantity (N), algebra (A), functions (F), modeling (incorporated into other standards), geometry (G), and statistics and probability (S). The CCS for grade 7 and grade 8 mathematics provide detailed expectations by grade level. These standards are coded by the grade level, 7 or 8, followed by RP (ratios and proportional relationships), NS (the number system), EE (expressions and equations), F (functions), G (geometry), or SP (statistics and probability).

Numerous mathematics CCS are represented in this book, in whole or in part. These standards are listed below, followed by the chapter(s) most relevant to that standard.

8.SP.2   Know that straight lines are widely used to model relationships between two quantitative variables. For scatter plots that suggest a linear association, informally fit a straight line, and informally assess the model fit by judging the closeness of the data points to the line. (Chapter 4)

8.F.3   Interpret the equation $y = mx + b$ as defining a linear function, whose graph is a straight line; give examples of functions that are not linear. (Chapters 4, 6)

7.EE.3   Solve multi-step and real-life and mathematical problems posed with positive and negative rational numbers in any form (whole numbers, fractions, and decimals), using tools strategically. Apply properties of operations to calculate with numbers in any form, convert between forms as appropriate; and assess the reasonableness of answers using mental computation and estimation strategies. (Chapters 4, 6)

7.EE.4   Use variables to represent quantities in a real-world or mathematical problem and construct simple equations and inequalities to solve problems by reasoning about the quantities. (Chapter 4)

A-REI.3   Solve linear equations and inequalities in one variable, including equations with coefficients represented by letters. (Chapter 4)

F-IF.2   Use function notation, evaluate functions for inputs in their domains, and interpret statements that use function notation in terms of a context. (Chapters 4, 8)

F-BF.1   Write a function that describes a relationship between two quantities. (Chapter 4)

F-LE.1b   Recognize situations in which one quantity changes at a constant rate per unit interval relative to another. (Chapter 4)

F-LE.5   Interpret the parameters in a linear or exponential function in terms of context. (Chapters 4, 6)

S-ID.7   Interpret the slope (rate of change) and the intercept (constant term) of a linear model in the context of the data. (Chapter 4)

7.G.6   Solve real-world and mathematical problems involving area, volume and surface area of two-dimensional and three-dimensional objects composed of triangles, quadrilaterals, polygons, cubes, or prisms. (Chapter 5)

8.G.7   Apply the Pythagorean Theorem to determine unknown side lengths in right triangles in real-world and mathematical problems in two and three dimensions. (Chapter 5)

8.NS.1   Understand informally that every number has a decimal expansion; the rational numbers are those with decimal expansions that terminate in 0s or eventually repeat. Know that other numbers are called irrational. (Chapter 5)

8.EE.2   Use square root and cube root symbols to represent solutions to equations of the form $x^2 = p$ and $x^3 = p$, where p is a positive rational number. Evaluate square roots of small perfect squares and cube roots of small perfect cubes. Know that $\sqrt{2}$ is irrational.

N-RN.1   Explain how the definition of the meaning of rational exponents follows from extending the properties of integer exponents to those values, allowing for a notation for radicals in terms of rational exponents. (Chapter 5)

G-CO.3   Given a rectangle, parallelogram, trapezoid, or regular polygon, describe the rotations and reflections that carry it onto itself. (Chapter 5)

G-MG.1   Use geometric shapes, their measures, and their properties to describe objects. (Chapter 6)

G-MG.3   Apply geometric methods to solve design problems. (Chapter 6)

N-Q.1   Use units as a way to understand problems and to guide the solution of multi-step problems; choose and interpret units consistently in formulas; choose and interpret the scale and origin in graphs and data displays (Chapter 6)

N-Q.2   Define appropriate quantities for the purpose of descriptive modeling. (Chapter 6)

F-LE.1   Distinguish between situations that can be modeled with linear functions and with exponential functions. (Chapter 6)

F-LE.1c   Recognize situations in which a quantity grows or decays by a constant percent rate per unit interval relative to another. (Chapter 6)

S-MD.5b   Evaluate and compare strategies on the basis of expected values. (Chapter 7)

A-CED.4   Rearrange formulas to highlight a quantity of interest, using the same reasoning as in solving equations. (Chapter 8)

F-IF.2   Use function notation, evaluate functions for inputs in their domains, and interpret statements that use function notation in terms of a context. (Chapter 8)

F-IF.6   Calculate and interpret the average rate of change of a function (presented symbolically or as a table) over a specified interval. Estimate the rate of change from a graph. (Chapter 8)

APPENDIX D
A Few Notable Organizations and Resources
Dedicated to Mathematics, Education, Special Education and Career Planning

American Mathematical Society (AMS)
https://www.ams.org/home/page

MATHCOUNTS Foundation
https://www.mathcounts.org

Mathematics Association of America (MAA)
https://www.maa.org/member-communities/high-school-teachers

National Association of Special Education Teachers (NASET)
https://www.naset.org/fileadmin/user_upload/Autism_Series/Assist_tech/Assist
iveTech_for_Students_W_Autism.pdf

National Council of Teachers of Mathematics (NCTM)
https://www.nctm.org/About/

Occupational Outlook Handbook (about careers, requirements, skills, salaries)
https://www.bls.gov/ooh/a-zindex.htm

Priorities for Equitable Instruction: 2021 & Beyond
https://achievethecore.org/page/3267/2020-21-priority-instructional-content-in-
english-language-arts-literacy-and-mathematics

ThoughtCo.com – In 2018, ThoughtCo received an Award in the General
Education category and a Davey Award in the Education category.
https://www.thoughtco.com/

Tools for Teachers – Smarter Balanced
https://www.smartertoolsforteachers.org/

youcubed (resources to excite students about mathematics)
https://www.youcubed.org

APPENDIX E
Additional Extension Activities

The activities listed here provide additional resources for students, parents or teachers.

Vocabulary overview:

1. Quiz yourself. If you looked back at the glossary, how many vocabulary words are you comfortable defining in your own words?

2. If you find any vocabulary words that you are uncomfortable with, discuss them with a friend. Can you also help a friend with any vocabulary words that they are uncomfortable with?

3. Knowing math vocabulary can help you succeed. Can you draw or depict the words that are more challenging for you in a creative way? Can you define them in your own way? Doing this will help store them in your long term memory. Always remember – with a growth mindset, you have limitless potential!

Five ways in which teachers are using drones in the classroom
http://edu4.me/five-ways-in-which-teachers-are-using-drones-in-the-classroom/

Using echo from drones to determine shape of room
https://phys.org/news/2020-02-drones-room.html

Observe a drone and graph its movement
https://www.youtube.com/watch?v=bJKur3pbeVQ

Using drones to teach calculus
https://www.thedronegirl.com/2019/10/18/drone-math-lesson/

APPENDIX F
ABOUT THE AUTHOR

Jeanne has enjoyed life as an educational leader, teacher, actuarial analyst, research chemist, and volunteer at a local children's museum. Through her books, she hopes to link knowledge and skills to inspire interdisciplinary learning and spark meaningful discussion.

As an undergraduate, Jeanne double majored in mathematics and chemistry. She has a master's degree in education from Elms College, and a post-master's degree in educational leadership from Westfield State University.

Jeanne lives in Massachusetts with her husband and their very sweet Scottish Terrier named Rocky.

You can follow Jeanne and Rocky at: jeanneholmberg.com

THE END

Coming in 2022 by Jeanne Holmberg

"Curious Isabella"

A Picture Book For A Young Audience That Blends

Science, Art, And Whimsy

Made in the USA
Middletown, DE
24 November 2021

52825911R00060